NAOMI AND FLY HAVE BECOME SEPARATED FROM THEIR FRIENDS AND ARE LOST IN THE SECRET PATHWAYS TO THE NEXT VILLAGE. LUCKILY THE BLUE STAR WARRIORS CAN COMMUNICATE THROUGH RAITETSU'S MAGICAL ROKOLOI.

CATAPULTED INTO A
TREETOP, JIM IS SURE
THAT HIS FIRST VISION
OF SUIRAN, THE WINGED
PANTHER, WILL BE THE
VERY LAST THING HE
WILL EVER SEE.

JIM AND DOUG COMBINE THEIR POWERS TO ATTACK THE TWO POISONOUS BUTTERFLIES SENT BY GENERAL URO. EVEN THE MAGIC OF THE TELAAM IS NOT ENOUGH TO HOLD THEM BACK.

THE FOOL

When Hanata, seer of the Telaam, draws the Fool from her deck of Vermonian cards, Doug and Jim's fate becomes all too clear.

VERMONIA

Release of the Red Phoenix

YOYO

ヨーヨー

WALKER
BOOKS

FIRST PUBLISHED IN 2010 BY WALKER BOOKS LTD
87 VAUXHALL WALK, LONDON SE11 5HJ

2 4 6 8 10 9 7 5 3 1

COPYRIGHT © 2010 RAITETSU MEDIA LLC AND RAY PRODUCTIONS LTD
NEW YORK AND TOKYO

THIS BOOK HAS BEEN TYPESET IN CCLADRONN ITALIC

PRINTED AND BOUND IN CHINA

BRITISH LIBRARY CATALOGUING IN PUBLICATION DATA: A CATALOGUE RECORD FOR THIS
BOOK IS AVAILABLE FROM THE BRITISH LIBRARY

ISBN 978-1-4063-2179-1

WWW.WALKER.CO.UK
WWW.VERMONIA.COM

THE ATTACK IS EASY TO SEE. WE HAVE TO GET TO NAOMI AND FLY!

WE HAVE TO HELP HER. BUTABO, YOU'LL HAVE TO SHOW DOUG, JIM, AND RAINBOW THE WAY TO THE UMLI.

YES, HANATA.

LET'S HURRY BEFORE IT'S TOO LATE.

YES.

RAINBOW, ARE YOU READY?

.....?

THAT IS WHERE OUR ELDER, NAAMAN, WILL MEET US.

TO GET TO THE UMLI, YOU'LL NEED TO CROSS THE DESERT.

YOU WILL DEPART FROM XILO BEACH ON THE ORITSA.

I WONDER IF THE AQAMI PEOPLE ARE GOING TO HELP US TOO.

HEY, GUYS! WHEN I RELEASED SUIRAN, THE SUNKEN WARSHIP OF THE AQAMI ROSE TO THE SURFACE OF THE OCEAN.

??

YOU'VE GOT TO BE KIDDING!

BUT OF COURSE! NAAMAN MUST KNOW THAT THE AQAMI'S WARSHIP HAS SURFACED!

YES, THE VLESTE...

BUTABO, TELL NAAMAN ABOUT THE VLESTE. TRY TO MAKE CONTACT WITH THE AQAMI.

RIGHT AWAY.

......

THERE'S NO TIME TO LOSE.

WAIT!

WHAT IS IT?

RAINBOW, TELL ME.

DON'T JUST RUSH OFF.

WHAT ARE YOU SAYING?

JIM NEEDS TO STAY BEHIND.

WHY?

YOU'RE WOUNDED, JIM...

YOU DON'T CARE ABOUT YOUR SHOULDER, BUT I DO.

IF HE HAS TO FIGHT IN HIS CONDITION, HE'LL NEVER GET BETTER.

JIM...

CAN'T SOMEONE PLEASE CONVINCE HIM?

HIS INJURIES WON'T HOLD HIM BACK.

!?

SHE'S WORRIED ABOUT YOU.

SHE FEELS RESPONSIBLE FOR YOUR GETTING HURT...

...WHEN YOU PROTECTED HER.

RAINBOW?

SO YOU DO CARE.

J-J-JIM...

JIM, THERE'S NO TIME.

BUT...

RAINBOW, IS THIS WHAT'S WORRYING YOU?

.....

JIM, PUT YOUR HAND IN MINE.

10

HOLD IT AGAINST YOUR WOUND LIKE THIS.

IS THIS RIGHT?

SUIRAN, WHY HAVE YOU GIVEN ME THIS GLOVE?

TAKE A LOOK AT MY SHOULDER.

IT'S HEALED PERFECTLY!

ARE YOU SURE, DOUG?

WOW! MY SHOULDER DOESN'T HURT ANYMORE.

CAN A GLOVE REALLY HAVE HEALING POWER?

WHAT ABOUT HERE?

AND HERE?

CAN I FIX DOUG'S SCRATCH?

USE THIS NEW POWER WISELY.

YOUR POWER COMES FROM THE FORCE YOU SHARE WITH SUIRAN.

I KNEW YOU'D COME TO HELP.

I DON'T FEEL SO GOOD.

I'VE GOT YOU, JIM.

RAITETSU!

I SEE. WELL, SHE CERTAINLY LOOKS STRONG.

LET'S HOPE WE CAN TRUST HER.

MIRANDA'S FAMILY HAVE ALWAYS BEEN THE GUARDIAN WARRIORS OF THE UMLI.

HURRY, NOW! WE MUST FOLLOW THE OTHERS UNDERGROUND.

HURRY. WE CAN'T SUSTAIN THE PROTECTIVE BARRIER ANY LONGER.

PLEASE COME THIS WAY.

COULD THIS GIRL REALLY BE THE ONE FROM BLUE STAR?

WELCOME, YOUNG WARRIORS. I AM UMNIDA, ELDER OF THE UMLI.

I'M AFRAID OUR BARRIER OF FIRE COULD NOT HELP US AGAINST ATTACK FROM GENERAL URO'S ARMY. NOW OUR VILLAGE IS DESTROYED.

IT IS NOT YOUR FAULT.

UMNIDA, I'M SORRY WE COULD NOT HAVE COME SOONER TO HELP. PERHAPS IF WE HAD...

THIS FIGHT IS OUR DESTINY.

HMMPH. AND SO WAS HELP FROM BLUE STAR.

MIKO!

IF THIS BLUE STAR WARRIOR HAD NOT TAKEN SO LONG, WE MIGHT HAVE HAD SUZAKU, THE RED PHOENIX, BY OUR SIDE BY NOW. OR SO OUR SACRED BOOK, THE UMLIAD, PREDICTED.

LOOK AT HER. CAN YOU DOUBT HER NOBILITY? SHE IS CARING FOR OUR WOUNDED.

MAYBE...

MIKO, WHAT ARE YOU GRUMBLING ABOUT?

SHE'S HERE NOW. WHAT MORE CAN YOU ASK?

25

I'M SORRY, HONORED GUEST, BUT MIKO IS VERY IRRITABLE. FORGIVE HER.

MIRANDA, LET ME GO!

OK.

!?

THEY'RE TWINS.

NAOMI.

YES?

THERE ARE TWO OF THEM.

I ASK FOR YOUR FORGIVENESS TOO. EVERYONE IS SO TIRED FROM FIGHTING.

REST NOW, WHILE I TALK WITH THE ELDER, UMNIDA.

.....

OK.

DON'T WORRY ABOUT WHAT MIKO SAID.

I'M ALL RIGHT.

THESE PAINTINGS ON THE WALL SHOW OUR FESTIVALS.

IT'S OK. I KNOW THAT TERRIBLE THINGS ARE HAPPENING NOW.

I'M SORRY MY SISTER WAS SO RUDE TO YOU BACK THERE.

OH! IT'S YOU.

I SAW YOU LOOKING AT THE WALL PAINTINGS. GUARDIAN WARRIORS LIKE FLY COME WITH THEIR BARDS TO OUR FESTIVAL, THE UMVRAT.

ARE THOSE PEOPLE SINGING?

MY NAME'S KHANN, AND MY SISTER'S NAME IS MIKO.

I'M NAOMI. NICE TO MEET YOU.

28

33

I SAW MY GUARDIAN IN A DREAM.

ARE YOU ALL RIGHT, NAOMI?

FLY...

I...

WHAT CAN I DO?

HOW DO I ESCAPE FROM THIS PLACE?

THIS CAPTAIN ACIDULOUS SCARES ME. WHERE IS HE TAKING ME?

I KNOW HE'S GOING TO USE ME TO STEAL FROM MY GUARDIAN, TO TRY TO GAIN RUKA'S GIFT OF FORESIGHT.

YOU'RE COMING WITH ME ON THIS TAKKADRA.

SHOULD I RUN FOR IT?

NO WAY
I'M GETTING
ON THAT!!

NO ONE COULD
ESCAPE FROM HERE.

MIKO, WE SHOULDN'T PUT HER IN DANGER!

BOTH OF YOU, STOP!

THERE IS NOTHING ELSE WE CAN DO!

NAOMI...

I'LL GO.

ENOUGH!

IF I CAN SAVE YOU ALL, I WILL.

YOU HEARD MIKO. WE'VE GOT NO CHOICE.

I HAVE TO DO WHATEVER IT TAKES!

MIKO, LET'S GIVE HER...

I WON'T LET YOU GO OUT THERE ALONE.

YOU MEAN...?

?

WE HAVE SOMETHING FOR YOU.

NAOMI, FOLLOW US.

WHEN URO CAME, WE MADE ALL THE WEAPONS FOR OUR ALLIES.

IN THE DAYS OF OUR BEGINNING, THE GODS GAVE THE UMLI FIRE AND THE FORGE.

WE ARE SKILLED METALWORKERS.

IT'S A SHIELD OF BRONZE.

THIS IS A MASTERPIECE THAT WE NEVER SHARED.

OUR CHRONICLES TOLD US IT WAS TO BE SAVED FOR A DESTINED WARRIOR WHO WOULD COME... A WOMAN WARRIOR.

BE PEACEFUL IN YOUR MIND. YOU HAVE THE MOST POWERFUL DEFENSE THE UMLI HAVE EVER MADE, AND WE WILL BE CLOSE BEHIND YOU AND READY TO FIGHT.

WE BESTOW THIS UPON YOU. MAY IT HELP YOU IN YOUR MISSION TO RELEASE SUZAKU, THE EMISSARY OF FRASINELLA, OUR GREAT MOTHER, QUEEN OF VERMONIA.

46

OK.

EVEN MIKO NOW WISHES ME WELL.

I'M SCARED.

BUT I MUST OVERCOME MY FEAR AND FIGHT.

I'M ASKING YOU NICELY.

COME ON, LET'S TAKE OUR POSITIONS.

I'M HERE. NOW PUT OUT THE FIRES!

YOU GO FIRST, AND WE'LL FOLLOW USING THE SIDE TUNNEL.

......

I'M SURE HE DOESN'T INTEND TO KILL YOU.

OK.

I MUST PROTECT HER!

KYUBI, STAY CLOSE BEHIND NAOMI AND USE YOUR NINE-TAIL POWER. READY?

DO NOT DISOBEY ME.

PUT OUT THE FIRE!

WE'LL SEE ABOUT THAT!!

I HAVE MY ORDERS. GENERAL URO DEMANDS THAT YOU COME BEFORE HIM.

I DON'T WANT TO VANISH INTO DARKNESS.

WHO'S SPEAKING?

AM I INSIDE THIS MONSTER'S THOUGHTS?

ARE YOU ALL RIGHT?

YES...

FLY, THERE'S NO TIME TO REST!

BROTHER, LOOK AT THE DARKNESS! SOMETHING DANGEROUS IS COMING OUR WAY.

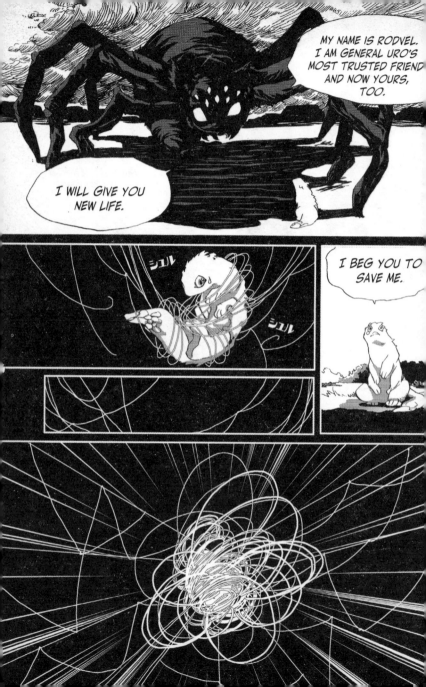

YOU DESERVE TO BE THE MASTER OF THE MIDNIGHT SWORD.

IT'S BEAUTIFUL.

NAAMAN ASKED ME TO GIVE IT TO YOU. LET IT REPLACE THE SWORD THAT WAS BROKEN IN DEFENDING US.

I WILL BE HONORED TO FIGHT WITH IT.

I GUESS WE COULD. NAOMI HAS THE OTHER.

YEAH, HERE IT IS.

IF WE CAN'T TRUST YOU, WHO CAN WE TRUST?

THANK YOU. IN THIS WAY WE CAN SERVE YOU. WE WILL GIVE IT BACK UPON YOUR RETURN.

AND NOW, DOUG, WILL YOU GIVE ME YOUR ROKOLOS?

MY MOTHER SAYS THAT SHE WANTS TO KEEP YOU INFORMED OF HER READING OF THE VERMONIAN CARDS.

IT'S SO COLD HERE.

BUT RODVEL HAS ALREADY GONE TO THE UMLI.

...ARUSSHA.

I HAVE BEEN WAITING FOR YOU, CAPTAIN ACIDULOUS.

I SUPPOSE THIS IS THE GIRL?

!?

WEAR MY CLOAK.

IT WILL WARM YOU UP.

COLD? HERE, TAKE THIS.

.....

THIS IS A GREAT HONOR.

YOU, MELANIE, NOT YOUR THREE FRIENDS.

!!?

NOW YOU MUST OPEN YOUR DREAM.

IT'S YOU!!

DID YOU MISS ME?

!!!

GIVE ME THE KEY. QUICKLY!

ONCE I HAVE YOU, I WON'T LET YOU GO.

WHAT A PITY.

YOU'VE RELEASED YOUR BODY TO ME, BUT NOT ALL YOUR SPIRIT.

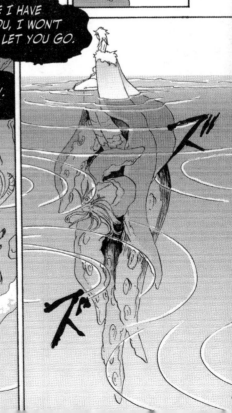

THAT'S
GOOD.

MEL.

MEL, FOLLOW
RUKA'S ADVICE.

MELANIE...

AWAKE AMONG
YOUR FRIENDS.

EVERYTHING HAS WORKED AS PLANNED, MY CAPTAIN.

ONCE I GAVE THE GIRL MY CAPE, IT WAS EASIER TO ENTER HER DREAM.

WHEN WE OWN RUKA'S SPIRIT...

...WE CONTROL THE MESSAGES SHE SENDS TO MELANIE.

THEN BOTH SHE AND RUKA WILL FIGHT FOR US.

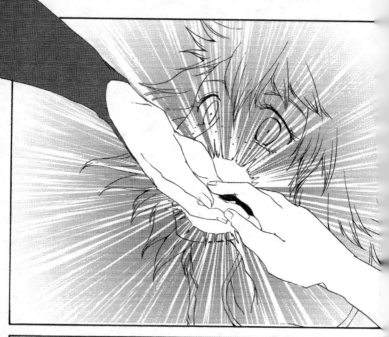

WHEN SHE'S RESTED, TAKE HER TO THE DESERT TO CONFRONT HER FORMER FRIENDS.

ARGHHH!!

AFTER THAT, BRING HER TO ME. I WILL TAKE HER TO RELEASE RUKA COMPLETELY.

YES, CAPTAIN.

NAOMI!!

HE IS UNDER SOME OTHER CREATURE'S POWERS.

PLEASE, FLY. DON'T ATTACK HIM!

NAOMI!! TALK TO ME!

FLY!

HOW CAN YOU BE SO SURE?

THE DEAD TREE THAT SENDS FORTH ITS LEAVES ANEW.

WHAT HAPPENED TO ME?

DID I DIE?

YOU'VE FOUND MY PRISON. YOUR COMPASSION BROUGHT YOU TO ME.

NO, THE OPPOSITE.

LOOK AT THE BASE OF THE TREE.

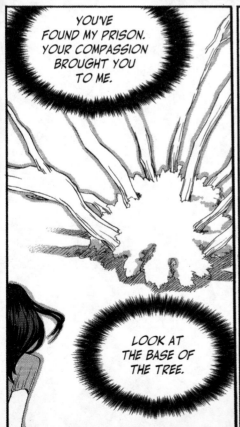

LOOK BEYOND YOUR SIGHT.

I'M TRYING, BUT...

AH!!

THERE IS ALWAYS A CONTROLLING HAND.

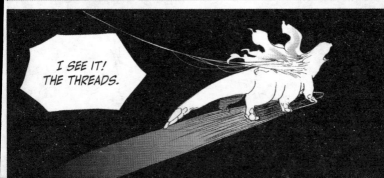

I SEE IT! THE THREADS.

DRAT!

IT'S OK.
I CUT THE
WEB.

NAOMI, ARE
YOU HURT?

I'VE LOST CONTROL OF CAUDACIS.

I'VE GOT YOU, LITTLE ONE.

HE WAS TORTURING ME AND YOU...

Zoop

IT'S OK. YOU'RE FREE.

MY FRIENDS ARE ALSO LINED UP AGAINST YOU.

FRIENDS? SHE CALLS ME A FRIEND...

IS IT SO STRANGE?

SUZAKU!

IT IS YOUR BRAVERY THAT BRINGS EVERYONE TOGETHER.

MIKO CALLED ME BY NAME.

NAOMI, THROW YOUR FIRE. WE'RE READY TO ATTACK!

THE GREATER THE STRENGTH OF OUR ATTACK, THE MORE POWERFULLY HE COUNTERS.

134

!?

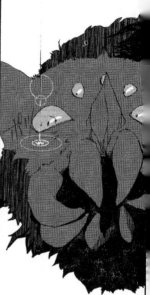

SURRENDER TO ME NOW. YOU CANNOT TRIUMPH.

?

RAIN?

YOU MUST...

HUH?!

IS IT YOU, ARUSSHA?

AND THIS GIRL? DON'T TELL ME SUZAKU HAS ESCAPED.

RODVEL, I HAVEN'T SEEN YOU IN YOUR TRUE FORM SINCE WE LEFT VERMONIA.

.....

HOW COULD YOU LET THAT HAPPEN!?

SHUT UP, ARUSSHA. YOU KNOW NOTHING.

EXCUSE ME...

YOU ARE TRULY PATHETIC.

SHUT UP! YOU'RE USELESS.

YOUR MISSION WAS TO KEEP HER IMPRISONED. GREAT JOB, RODVEL.

OUR CAPTAIN IS GOING TO CRUSH YOU LIKE A BUG.

HEY!

GOOD. BECAUSE I DON'T NEED YOUR HELP.

LISTEN, I DIDN'T COME HERE TO HELP YOU.

I'M NOT SO SURE OF THAT, SEEING THAT YOU COULDN'T EVEN DEFEAT THEM IN YOUR TRUE FORM.

THIS RAIN IS NOT OF MY MAKING.

AS FOR THIS LOUSY RAIN... WILL YOU PLEASE STOP IT? YOU KNOW I HATE RAIN.

I CAN'T.

WHAT'S THAT?

IT'S NAOMI'S ROKOLOS!

!!?

THE VILLAGE! IT'S COMPLETELY DESTROYED.

WHERE ARE THE UMLI? HAS ANYONE SURVIVED?

NAOMI!

THERE'S SO MUCH SMOKE, I CAN'T SEE A THING.

NAOMI! FLY!

LET'S GO THIS WAY.

YA... HAAAAH!!

OH, NO! STOP. YOU'RE SCARING ME. I'LL RELEASE HER. HEH, HEH, HEH...

ISN'T THIS FUN, RODVEL?

THAT GUY'S GOT SUIRAN'S POWER OF WIND.

EH!?

NO!

GIVE HER BACK TO US!

.....

I DON'T BELIEVE IT. MEL ISN'T WITH YOU. YOU ONLY CONTROL HER.

SHUT UP.

YOU'LL BEAT HER LATER. THIS WAS JUST SUPPOSED TO BE A DEMONSTRATION.

NAOMI, GET A GRIP. WHY ARE YOU FIGHTING HER?

COME WITH ME.

WE'LL HAVE SOME FUN WITH HER LATER.

YOU'LL NEVER BEAT ME, MEL! DO YOU HEAR ME?!

RELEASING RUKA AND FIGHTING HAS EXHAUSTED YOU.

HEY! ARE YOU GOING TO BE ILL?

GASP...

GASP...

IF RODVEL HADN'T STEPPED IN...

I DREAMED...

A DREAM?

WHAT DID YOU DREAM?

I COULD SEE OUR FUTURE.

165

SHE'S FAINTED.

HEY!

TELL US WHAT IT BRINGS.

LET'S TAKE HER BACK WITH US TO THE CAPTAIN'S CASTLE.

HMM, HOW IS EVERYONE? WHERE'S JIM?

HE'S RESTING RIGHT OVER THERE. HE USED TOO MUCH OF SUIRAN'S POWERS ON THE WOUNDED VILLAGERS AND HE'S VERY WEAK.

HE HAS TO BE MORE CAREFUL HOW HE USES THE GLOVE.

HE HAS VERY LITTLE LIFE FORCE LEFT.

WILL HE BE OK?

NAOMI...

......

SLEEPING IS THE BEST CURE FOR JIM. WE'RE JUST GOING TO LET HIM BE.

OK.

FLY?

RAINBOW'S GETTING SOME FOOD READY.

GREAT. I'M STARVING. WOW. WHAT LUCK. EVERYONE'S OK.

IT'S FUNNY, ISN'T IT?

IT'S RIDICULOUS.

WE'VE BEEN TRYING SO HARD TO SAVE MEL, AND ALL THIS TIME SHE'S BEEN FIGHTING FOR URO.

BUT I THINK I KNOW WHY SHE DID IT, EVEN THOUGH SHE NEVER SAID SO HERSELF.

.....

WE WERE SO CLOSE.

OUR BAND, VERACITY, WAS GREAT.

THEN SUDDENLY SHE LEAVES US, FOR NO GOOD REASON.

WHEN HER FATHER BECOMES THE MAYOR, SHE SIMPLY WON'T BE ABLE TO HAVE SUCH PEOPLE AS HER FRIENDS.

!!?

NOTHING. LET'S GET OUT OF HERE.

?

WHAT'S WRONG?

SORRY.

SOON AFTER THIS, MEL'S FATHER DID WIN THE ELECTION.

AND MEL LEFT THE BAND.

BUT ALL THAT DIDN'T MATTER WHEN WE WERE REHEARSING. OR IN THE PARK.

AND EVEN THOUGH EVERY KID IN UNION CITY WAS AGAINST HER...

HOW COULD I HAVE?

IT WOULD'VE ONLY MADE IT MORE DIFFICULT BETWEEN HER AND HER FATHER.

SO WHY DIDN'T YOU TELL HER YOU KNEW WHAT WAS GOING ON?

...I TRIED TO STICK UP FOR HER, BUT SHE PUSHED ME AWAY.

SHE WAS EMBARRASSED, I GUESS.

I'M NOT SURE.

WHY DO I SUDDENLY SEE HANATA'S CARDS? WEIRD.

.....

DID YOU FIND A WAY TO LET HER KNOW YOU UNDERSTOOD?

FORTUNE TURNS THE WHEELS.

ONE WARRIOR RISES ON THE WINGS OF A GREAT BIRD. ANOTHER DESCENDS. THEY WILL MEET IN COMBAT.

I BET SHE COULD TELL.

YOU REALLY THINK SO?

YES, BUT SHE COULDN'T SHOW IT WITHOUT COMPROMISING HER LOYALTY TO HER FATHER. IT IS HARD WHEN LOVE PULLS YOU IN TWO DIRECTIONS.

ME
TOO.

LET'S EAT.
I'M HUNGRY.

I NEVER
THOUGHT
OF THAT.

MAYBE HANATA'S
CARDS ARE WRONG.

ARE YOU FEELING
STRONGER?

NAOMI, SIT
WITH ME.

MIKO STILL SENDS
ME DIRTY LOOKS.

MIKO!

.....

HAHAHA

MIKO, YOU ACTUALLY LIKE ME!

STOP THAT!

SIT DOWN NEXT TO ME. WHAT ARE YOU WAITING FOR?

A HA HA HA

JOIN US, NAOMI.

!!

NAOMI!!

I CAN'T BELIEVE YOU'RE HERE.

SATORIN!

POPULAR GIRL.

177

. . . . .

DID YOU GET A GOOD NIGHT'S SLEEP?

YOU AGAIN.

YOU'VE BEEN OVEREXERTING YOURSELF.

REST IS IMPORTANT.

THE CAPTAIN AWAITS YOU. FOLLOW ME.

YOU MEAN YOU NEED ME HEALTHY SO THAT I CAN DO WHAT YOU NEED.

GO TO THE END OF THE CORRIDOR TO THE GREAT HALL.

THERE, YOU WILL STAND BEFORE THE COUNCIL.

HAD WE NOT CAPTURED THE WATER FORCE, HAD RUKA BEEN WITH THEM, THEIR FORCE...

...MIGHT HAVE BEEN TOO MUCH.

.....

ATTENTION!

THEY FIGHT WITH THE POWER OF THREE OF THE FOUR PILLARS.

YOUR DERAS MANAGBO AND OMUS HAVE RETURNED FROM THEIR MISSION.

APOLOGIES FOR OUR TARDY ARRIVAL, CAPTAIN.

YOU STARTED WITHOUT US?

ARE YOU THE WATER GIRL WHO HAS JOINED OUR ARMY? I AM THE DERA MANAGBO.

???

UGLY CLOTHES.

I CANNOT ACCEPT ANY MORE FAILURES.

HERE ARE YOUR ORDERS. YOU MUST DESTROY THIS...

HEY!

HELLO?

!!

THEY'VE COMPLETELY FORGOTTEN ABOUT ME.

WHO'S THAT?

WHAT'S THAT LIGHT?

WHAT THE HECK?!

HELLO?

IS ANYONE THERE?

WHO'S TALKING TO ME?

JIM!? DOUG?!

THE ROKOLOS!

WHAT IS IT?

ARE YOU ALONE?

JIM, I'M SO HAPPY I FOUND YOU.

IRENU!

WHERE IS BUTABO?

I HAVE TO SPEAK TO HIM IMMEDIATELY.

IRENU, WE'RE ALL GATHERED. WHAT IS IT?

THE ELDERS ARE MEETING.

YOU HAVE TO COME BACK WITH UMNIDA TO OUR VILLAGE.

IT SOUNDS URGENT. WHAT'S HAPPENING?

WE HAVE FINALLY RECEIVED A MESSAGE FROM THE AQAMI.

THE GUARDIANS WERE SENT TO SAFEGUARD THESE FORCES.

FOUR PILLARS SUPPORT THIS TURTLE REALM. WATER, FIRE, THUNDER, AND WIND.

IT MUST BE RAITETSU SPEAKING THROUGH YOU.

I SEE.

I HAVE NO IDEA HOW I KNOW THIS.

WOW.

MAYBE...

IF URO GETS THE PILLARS, THE TURTLE REALM BECOMES A WASTELAND CONSUMED BY DARKNESS.

THAT'S WHY THEY HOLD HER. THEY WANT HER GUARDIAN'S KNOWLEDGE. AND THEN THEY'LL TRY TO FORCE EACH ONE OF US TO REVEAL WHAT WE KNOW.

BUT HOW DO WE PROTECT THE BOLIRIUM IF WE DON'T KNOW WHERE IT IS OR EVEN WHAT IT IS?

I'M NOT SURE. BUT, WITH MEL IN THEIR HANDS, OUR TASK IS MORE DIFFICULT.

WARRIORS OF BLUE STAR, IT IS IMPERATIVE THAT YOU JOIN THE MEETING OF THE ELDERS.

RETURN TO US WITH BUTABO AND UMNIDA.

NAOMI...

WHAT WERE YOU THINKING ABOUT?

.....

THANK YOU.

IT'S VERY COLD IN THE DESERT AT NIGHT.

NOTHING. I'M TOO TIRED TO THINK.

MEL ATTACKED US WITH WATER.

BUT URO ATTACKED WITH FIRE!

.....

EVERYTHING HAS STOPPED BURNING.

!!

IF MEL HADN'T USED WATER, WE MIGHT HAVE ALL BEEN BURNED ALIVE.

WHY DID SHE DO THAT?

ARE YOU SAYING SHE FOUND A WAY TO HELP US WITHOUT LETTING RODVEL KNOW?

I SO WANT TO BELIEVE IT'S TRUE.

IT MEANS SHE'S TRYING TO GET BACK TO US.

THAT WOULD BE INCREDIBLE IF IT'S TRUE.

BUT I COULD NOT FIND RUKA'S FULL PRESENCE WITHIN HER.

I FEAR THAT BOTH RUKA AND MEL ARE TOGETHER.

THIS IS WHAT IS SO STRANGE.

JIM! DOUG!

BUT BOTH ARE STILL IMPRISONED.

IF THIS IS SO...

COMING

SOON...